DADDY
For
changed
nappy
by
Rupert
Fawcett

ISBN: 9781909732339

DADDY

For every man who ever changed a nappy

by Rupert Fawcett

BB

DADDY, WOTCHOO DOING ?
I'M DOING A POOH, THOMAS
CAN I SEE IT ?
NO, DARLING. CLOSE THE DOOR
IS IT A BIG DADDY POOH ?
YES
CLUMPF
IS IT BWOWN ?
YES, IT'S BROWN
IS MUMMY GOING TO WIPE YOUR BOTTY ?
NO, DARLING
PEEP! PEEP! PEEP! PEEP!
CAN I WIPE YOUR BOTTY ?
DAVID, CAN I CALL YOU BACK LATER ? I'M IN A MEETING

HI, DARLING ! YOU LOOK NICE !
HERE, LET ME DO THAT !
THAT'S A NICE DRESS, IS IT NEW ?
I'LL COOK DINNER. YOU SIT DOWN AND RELAX
ALRIGHT, STEPHEN. YOU'RE AFTER SOMETHING. WHAT IS IT ?
SEX !
AND DON'T FORGET TO WASH THE KITCHEN FLOOR !
SHE DRIVES A HARD BARGAIN

1.
THIS IS A MOMENT TO SAVOUR ....
2.
THE CHILDREN ARE TUCKED UP IN BED. I'VE HAD A NICE SHOWER
3.
SARAH IS IN THE BATHROOM MAKING HERSELF GORGEOUS AND IT'S MY BIRTHDAY !
4.
IT'S AGES SINCE WE LAST MADE LOVE SO I WANT TO TAKE IT REALLY SLOW, WITH PLENTY OF FOREPLAY.
5.
SHE'S TAKING A LONG TIME, BUT WHAT'S THE RUSH? .....JUST SAVOUR THE MOMENT
6.
MEANWHILE, IN THE BATHROOM...
ZZZZZZ

I'M WIDING FWU DA WOODS ON MY HORSE!
HOPPITY HOP
BEAM
BEAM
THERE ARE BUNNYWABBITS PLAYING IN DA GWASS.....
SKIPPETY SKIP
PRIDE
PRIDE
AND SQUIWELS EATING NUTS IN DA TWEES.....
PRANCE PRANCE
GLOW
GLOW
AND LOTS OF PWITTY FLOWERS
HOPPETY HOP
BEAM
BEAM
OH LOOK, DES A SNAKE IN DA GWASS. I HAVE TO GET MY SWORD!
SKIPPETY SKIP
CHUCKLE
GIGGLE
I KILL YOU! STAB, STAB, STAB! I CUT OFF YOUR HEAD! I STAMP ON IT! STAMP, STAMP, STAMP. YOU'RE DEAD!
SHUDDER SHUDDER
PANIC PANIC

HI, DARLING!
STEPHEN, WE'VE GOT A PROBLEM WITH THE CHILDREN
IT'S MY FAULT... WE WERE LATE FOR NURSERY.... I WAS TRYING TO GET THOMAS INTO HIS CAR SEAT....
HE WAS WRIGGLING ALL OVER THE PLACE. ...ABIGAIL STARTED SCREAMING..... THEN HE BEGAN PINCHING HER
THEN I DROPPED MY PURSE IN THE GUTTER AND I JUST BLURTED IT OUT!
BLURTED **WHAT** OUT?
FUCK! FUCK! FUCK! FUCK!
FUCK! FUCK! FUCK! FUCK!

BILLS, BILLS, BILLS
I SPOKE TO ISOBEL TODAY. SHE'S REALLY FED UP
WHY?
TOM WAS EXPECTING A PROMOTION AT WORK AND SOMEONE ELSE GOT IT
SO HE'S STILL ON THE SAME SALARY AS ME HA! HA!
OH, POOR TOM!
THEY HAD INTENDED TO SEND CLARISSA TO A PRIVATE SCHOOL, BUT NOW SHE'LL HAVE TO GO TO THE LOCAL COMPREHENSIVE
TEE! HEE!
WHAT A SHAME!
THEY WERE HOPING TO BUY A NEW CAR THIS YEAR, SO THAT'S HAD TO GO ON ICE
HO! HO!
WHAT A DRAG!
BENEDICT IS TEETHING SO THEY'VE HAD BROKEN SLEEP FOR WEEKS. THEY'RE BOTH EXHAUSTED
HAW! HAW!
POOR THINGS!
CONSEQUENTLY SHE AND TOM HAVE BEEN ARGUING A LOT
I LOVE IT!
OH DEAR!
WHAT WOULD YOU LIKE FOR YOUR DINNER?
DON'T STOP NOW! THAT WAS THE MOST FUN I'VE HAD ALL WEEK!
ANYTHING!
ANY OTHER NEWS?

DADDY, BE A CWOCODILE !
NOT NOW, DARLING
DAILY NEWS INTEREST RATE DOWN
PWEASE BE A CWOCODILE DAD !
NOT NOW THOMAS. I'M READING
DAILY NEWS INTEREST RATE DOWN
PWEEEAASE !
DAILY NEWS INTEREST RATE DOWN
EEEEK !
GROWWL !
MUMMY ! MUMMY ! MUMMY !
DAILY NEWS INTEREST RATE DOWN
..DADDY'S BEING A CWOCODILE !
OOH, HOW EXCITING !
IF ONLY SHE WERE AS EASY TO PLEASE
DAILY NEWS INTEREST RATE DOWN

I'M GETTING MY BOAT WEDDY TO GO FWU DA JUNGLE !
I'M TAKING MY FWENDS !
DE DESK IS AN ELEPHANT ! DE COFFEE TABLE IS A LION'S HOUSE !
DE ARMCHAIR IS A MONKEY'S NEST. DE TELEVISION IS A SPACESHIP !
DE FIREPLACE IS A CAVE. DE CUPBOARD IS A DINOSAUR !
DE CARPET IS DA WIVER. I'M GETTING IN MY BOAT NOW !
WOTCHOO DOING , DADDY ?
STANDING ON A ROCK SO I DON'T GET MY FEET WET !
DAT'S NOT A WOCK ! DAT'S A CUSHION ! SILLY DADDY !
I'M WIDING DOWN DA WIVER IN MY BOAT....

ISN'T IT WONDERFUL TO SEE THE CHILDREN RUNNING AROUND ON THE BEACH NAKED
MMM, POOR THOMAS !
WHY 'POOR' THOMAS ?
HAVEN'T YOU NOTICED HOW TINY HIS WILLY IS ? IT'S HALF THE SIZE OF HIS FRIENDS' WILLIES
MY GOD ! YOU'RE RIGHT !
BUT I DON'T WANT TO PUT MY TWUNKS ON, DADDY !
JUST DO AS YOU'RE TOLD, THOMAS

THANK HEAVENS THE CHILDREN ARE ASLEEP AT LAST. I'M EXHAUSTED
HERE, LET ME GIVE YOU A HUG.
MMMM
MMMM
SQUEEZE!
NUZZLE!
GROPE!
SQUEEZE!
STOPPIT STEPHEN! CAN'T WE JUST HAVE AN INNOCENT HUG WITHOUT YOU GETTING ALL STEAMED UP?
OF **COURSE** WE CAN, DARLING!
BORING!
MMMM, THAT'S BETTER

OH, MY GOD ! STEPHEN !!
WHAT IS IT ?
ABIGAIL ! SHE'S BEEN PUTTING PAPER CLIPS IN HER MOUTH !
HAS SHE SWALLOWED ANY ?
I DON'T KNOW ! OPEN YOUR MOUTH DARLING !
I CAN'T SEE ANY ! SHE MIGHT HAVE SWALLOWED ONE ! WE'VE GOT TO GET HER X-RAYED !
HOLD ON ! I'VE GOT AN IDEA !
MY BABY ! MY BABY !
OK ! LIE HER DOWN !
SOB !

I WONDER HOW OFTEN THEY HAVE SEX ?
BLA BLA, BLAAHH !
...CONSTANTLY, IF THOSE SELF-SATISFIED GRINS ARE ANYTHING TO GO BY....... IT'S ALRIGHT FOR THEM, THEY DON'T HAVE **CHILDREN** !
BLAB, BLAB, BLAB.
THEY'LL PROBABLY BE AT IT HAMMER-AND-TONGS AS SOON AS THEY GET HOME..... JUST LIKE ME AND SARAH IN THE OLD DAYS.....
WE DID IT EVERYWHERE..... ON THE BEACH, IN THE CAR, ON THE KITCHEN TABLE.... UNTIL WE HAD THE **CHILDREN**
GABBLE ! GABBLE !
SIGH !
LOOK AT HIM ! I'D BE SMILING TOO IF I HAD NO RESPONSIBILITIES
GLOG GLOG
SHE'S GORGEOUS !..OF COURSE SHE IS, SHE DOESN'T HAVE TO SPEND ALL DAY CATERING TO THE NEEDS OF TWO DEMANDING CHILDREN AND MOPPING UP VOMIT
GLOG GLOG
I'D LIKE TO SEE THEM COPE WITH A COUPLE OF SCREAMING KIDS.... THAT'D WIPE THE SMILES OFF THEIR SMUG FACES
BLABBER ! BLABBER !
SUZY AND I HAVE SOME EXCITING NEWS....
...WE'RE EXPECTING THE PATTER OF TINY FEET !
WONDERFUL !
I LOVE YOU GOD
ACTUALLY.....
...IT'S TWINS !
YOU'RE JOKING !?
I'VE DIED AND GONE TO HEAVEN

COME ON, DARLING. OPEN YOUR MOUTH
SARAH'S A WONDERFUL MOTHER
MMMWWW
1
LOVELY STEWED APPLE FOR ABIGAIL. YUM, YUM, DELICIOUS
SHE'S SO PATIENT.....
MMMW
2
LOOK, HERE COMES AN AEROPLANE WITH STEWED APPLE ON. IT WANTS TO FLY INTO YOUR MOUTH WEEEEEEUUUUUUWWWW!
I DON'T KNOW HOW SHE DOES IT
MMMW
5
COME ON, DARLING. IF YOU DON'T EAT IT YOU'LL GET HUNGRY LATER
I WOULD HAVE GIVEN UP AGES AGO.
MMMWW
6

MUMMY MADE IT SPECIALLY. IT'LL MAKE YOU BIG AND STRONG AND BEAUTIFUL
... SO TOLERANT
MMMWW
3
COME ON SWEETHEART, OPEN YOUR MOUTH ! YOU LIKE APPLES !
....SO LOVING
MMMW
4
BE A GOOD GIRL AND OPEN YOUR MOUTH FOR MUMMY ! COME ON DARLING !
SHE'S AN ANGEL
MMMW
7
ALRIGHT THEN, STARVE ! SEE IF I CARE !
I SUPPOSE WE ALL HAVE OUR BREAKING POINT
8

I DON'T WANT TO GO TO MAX'S HOUSE!
BUT HE'S YOUR BEST FRIEND!
HE'S NOT MY BEST FWEND. I HATE HIM!
OF COURSE YOU DON'T HATE HIM
I DO HATE HIM! AND I HATE YOU AND DADDY AND ABIGAIL AND ALL MY FWENDS!
NOW YOU JUST BEI SILLY
I'M NOT BEING SILLY! YOU'RE SILLY!
THAT'S ENOUGH, THOMAS!
DON'T SAY THAT'S ENOUGH! DON'T SAY ANYFING! DON'T TALK TO ME! BE QUIET, DADDY!
I'LL BE QUIET IF YOU'RE QUIET!
I HATE YOU AND I HATE MUMMY AND I HATE ABIGAIL AND I HATE MAX AND HIS MUMMY AND DADDY AND I DON'T WANT TO GO TO HIS HOUSE!
REMEMBER HOW PLEASED WE WERE WHEN HE FIRST LEARNED TO SPEAK?

GOOD, I'M GLAD TO HEAR YOU ARE ALL WELL....
YES, WE'RE FINE...
ABIGAIL IS COMPLETELY WEANED NOW....
AND SHE SEEMS TO BE SLEEPING RIGHT THROUGH THE NIGHT..... TOUCH WOOD
THOMAS IS FINE.....
SOWWY, DADDY!
....STEPHEN'S TEACHING HIM SELF-DEFENCE
SOB!

THANKS FOR LOOKING AFTER THE CHILDREN, STEPHEN
BYE, DARLING!
DADDY, CAN WE WATCH A DVD ?
YOU COULD WATCH A DVD, OR YOU COULD ALL GATHER AROUND AND I'LL TELL YOU THE STORY OF THE WIBBLY, WOBBLY MONSTER ! GRRRRRROOWLL !
OR, WE COULD GET MY TOOLS OUT AND I WILL SHOW YOU HOW TO MAKE A MODEL BOAT OUT OF AN OLD PIECE OF WOOD
OR, WE COULD GET OUT THE OLD CLOTHES BOX AND DRESS UP AS PIRATES ON THE HIGH SEAS! NOW, WHICH IS IT GOING TO BE LANDLUBBERS ?
DVD!

I DON'T **BELIEVE** THAT GUY FROM NUMBER 9....
HE'S ONLY ABOUT 20 AND HE'S JUST GOT A BRAND NEW TOP-OF-THE-RANGE GTI ..... AND HE STILL LIVES WITH HIS PARENTS.... **WIMP!**
WONDERFUL! HE CAN'T GET IT STARTED!
WHAT'S THE JOKE ?
HA!
THAT COCKY CHARACTER FROM NUMBER 9. HE'S GOT A BRAND NEW £18,000 CAR COVERED WITH FINS AND SPOILERS AND IT WON'T START !
POOR CHAP , MUST HAVE A FLAT BATTERY
'POOR CHAP' SHE SAYS, HA ! SERVES HIM RIGHT ! **HEY** ! WHAT'S SARAH DOING OUT THERE ? SHE'S GOING OVER TO HIM ! WHAT'S SHE GOT IN HER HAND?
MY JUMP LEADS !!
DADDY ! DADDY ! CUDDLE !
DES MUMMY TALKING TO A MAN !
WHY DOES SHE HAVE TO SPOIL EVERYTHING ?
YES , THOMAS

....'AND WHO'S BEEN SLEEPING IN MY BED ?' CRIED THE MUMMY BEAR...
WHAT A WONDERFUL PHOTO OPPORTUNITY ! I'LL GET THE CAMERA !
KEEP STILL, ABIGAIL ! STOP WRIGGLING, THOMAS !
LET ME DOWN !
MUMMY ! WHAAAA !
STOP PULLING ABIGAIL'S SLEEVE !
WHAAAAAA !
THOMAS, LET GO OF MY GLASSES ! ABIGAIL, YOU'RE PULLING MY HAIR !
WHAAAA !
LET ME DOWN !
WHAAAAA !
OOUUCH !
AAAAAAH
ALRIGHT EVERYBODY AS YOU WERE !

I DON'T WANT YOU WEARING YOUR NEW HELMET IN THE HOUSE, THOMAS.
ALRIGHT, BUT YOU MUST TAKE IT OFF FOR DINNER.
VERY WELL. JUST THIS ONCE, BUT YOU MUST TAKE IT OFF FOR YOUR BATH.
DON'T BE RIDICULOUS, THOMAS. OF COURSE YOU CAN'T WEAR YOUR HELMET IN BED.
NO, THOMAS. YOU CANNOT WEAR YOUR HELMET TO SCHOOL TOMORROW.
DO YOU THINK I'M TOO HARD ON HIM ?

ALRIGHT CHILDREN YOU'VE EATEN YOUR LUNCH VERY WELL. NOW YOU CAN BOTH HAVE A JELLY BABY
DAMN! THERE'S ONLY ONE PINK ONE LEFT
WHICH COLOUR WOULD YOU LIKE, THOMAS ?
NOT THE PINK ! NOT THE PINK ! NOT THE PINK !
YOWZA !
BLACK
WHICH COLOUR WOULD YOU LIKE, ABIGAIL ?
NOT THE PINK ! NOT THE PINK ! NOT THE PINK!
MUNCH MUNCH
RED!
YOWZA ! YOWZA ! YOWZA!
MUNCH
ADMIT IT STEPHEN; YOU'RE HAVING A GOOD DAY
MUNCH MUNCH

NOW, NOW, CHILDREN... CALM DOWN. NO KICKING!
1.
I'VE BEEN LOOKING FOR SOMETHING DECENT FOR THE CHILDREN TO WATCH ON T.V. THIS AFTERNOON...
NO HAIR-PULLING!
2.
...THERE'S ABSOLUTELY NOTHING!
NO PINCHING!
3.
EVERY PROGRAMME – EVEN THE CARTOONS CONTAIN VIOLENCE IN SOME FORM OR OTHER...
NO SCRATCHING!
4.
LET'S FACE IT; TOM AND JERRY IS VERY VIOLENT!
ABSOLUTELY, DARLING. NO BITING!
5.
I'M SORRY, BUT I DON'T WANT OUR CHILDREN WATCHING THAT SORT OF THING!
I QUITE AGREE. YOU DON'T KNOW WHAT SORT OF INFLUENCE IT'S GOING TO HAVE. NO GOUGING, THOMAS!
6.

THOMAS ! GIVE THAT TO ME !
COME ON ! GIVE IT TO DADDY !
THIS IS NOT FUNNY THOMAS. NOW, BE A GOOD BOY AND GIVE IT TO DADDY
THOMAS ! I'M WARNING YOU

FICTION
BIOGRAPHY
THIS LOOKS LIKE A GOOD BOOK FOR SARAH !
IT COULD IMPROVE OUR MARRIAGE NOT TO MENTION OUR SEX LIFE
I BOUGHT YOU A PRESENT, DARLING !
YOU REALLY DON'T KNOW ME AT ALL DO YOU ?
HOW TO PLEASE YOUR MAN
WHOOPS

DADDY, WAKE UP. IT'S DAYTIME !
OH, GOD ! ANOTHER DAY !
COME ON !
ANOTHER DAY OF FINANCIAL INSECURITY. ANOTHER DAY OF ROBBING PETER TO PAY PAUL...
WAKE UP !
ANOTHER DAY OF WORKING OUT HOW WE CAN GET TO THE END OF THE MONTH WITHOUT EXCEEDING OUR OVERDRAFT LIMIT
COME ON, DADDY !
ALRIGHT, THOMAS
WAKE UP MUMMY !
IF THE POSTMAN HAS BROUGHT ANY MORE BILLS I'M GOING TO SCREAM
ALRIGHT, CHILDREN. LET'S GO DOWNSTAIRS FOR BREAKFAST !
AAA AAAA AARGH !

MOAN ! MOAN ! GROAN !
WOW, SARAH'S REALLY PASSIONATE TONIGHT !
CREEK, CREEK, CREEK,
MOAN ! MOAN ! OOOOH ! AAARGH !
THIS IS JUST LIKE THE OLD DAYS, BEFORE THE CHILDREN. BRILLIANT !
CREEKETTY, CREEKETTY, CREEKETTY,
STOP STEPHEN ! STOP ! I CAN'T GO ON !
WHAT'S THE MATTER, DARLING ?
THERE'S SOMETHING DIGGING INTO MY BACK
CLICK !
WHAT IS IT ?
I DON'T KNOW
THERE !
POSTMAN PAT'S DELIVERY VAN. SO MUCH FOR PASSION.

HELLO!
HI!
HI!
BIFF!
WHAT WOULD EVERYONE LIKE TO DRINK ?
COKE!
HERE WE ARE!
DADDY, HELP!
NAUGHTY BOY, SAM
I'LL GET A CLOTH
IT'S WARM
ONE OF THESE DAYS I'M GOING TO THROTTLE THAT BOY
NOW, NOW, CALM DOWN AND TAKE THESE SAUSAGE ROLLS THROUGH. DON'T GIVE ANY TO THE CHILDREN. THEY'RE EXTREMELY HOT.
WE WERE JUST ADMIRING YOUR GARDEN, STEPHEN
YOU MUST LET US KNOW YOUR SECRET
OH, THANK YOU. HERE, SAM, WOULD YOU LIKE A SAUSAGE ROLL ?

IT'S BEEN A WONDERFUL WEEKEND
TWO WHOLE DAYS WITHOUT THE CHILDREN. IT'S BEEN SO PEACEFUL
AND IT ALL COMES TO AN END IN AN HOUR WHEN MY MOTHER BRINGS THEM HOME
THOMAS, LEAVE ABIGAIL ALONE!
SIGH
STOP PINCHING HER! ABIGAIL, STOP SCRIBBLING ON THE WALLS!
STOP SPITTING, THOMAS! ABIGAIL, GET YOUR HEAD OUT OF THE TOILET!
STEPHEN, WHAT ON EARTH ARE YOU DOING?
WARMING UP!

DADDY'S HOME!
HOW'S MY LITTLE DARLING?
WHEEEEEEE!
EEEEEE!
OH! WHERE'S ABIGAIL GONE? I CAN'T SEE HER!
HEE, HEE, HEE, HEE,
SEE-SAW SEE-SAW SEE-SAW SEE-SAW
BE GENTLE WITH HER DARLING! SHE'S JUST HAD A FEED!

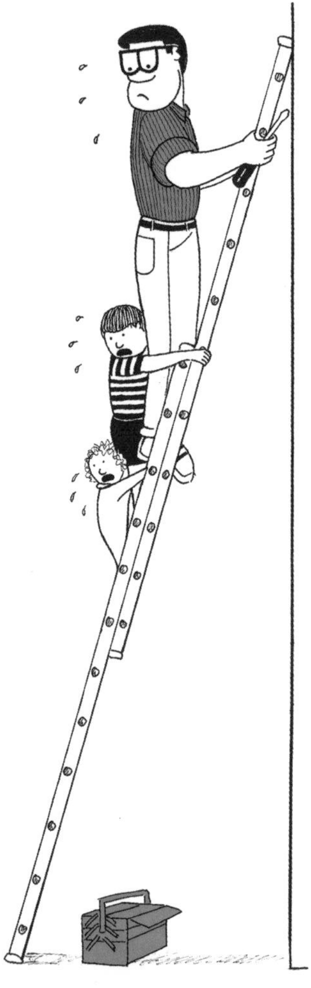

I DON'T THINK SHE'S BREATHING! I CAN'T SEE ANY MOVEMENT!
POKE HER!
HARDER! SHAKE HER, STEPHEN
SHAKE SHAKE
PHEEEW!
WHAT A RELIEF!
WHAAAAA!!
TWO HOURS LATER...
GOOOO TOOO SLEEEEEEP
WHAAAA AAAAAH!
SOB!

HI!
HI, DARLING!
I GOT THE CHILDREN TO BED ON TIME AND I'VE DONE THE WASHING UP...
I'VE ALSO HUNG UP ALL THE DAMP WASHING AND PUT AWAY THE DRY....
...AND CHANGED THE SHEETS ON OUR BED AND TIDIED AWAY THE CHILDREN'S TOYS
THAT'S THE KIND OF STUFF I DO EVERY DAY, STEPHEN. WHAT DO YOU WANT, A MEDAL ?
A LITTLE PAT ON THE HEAD AND A 'WELL DONE, DARLING,' WOULD HAVE BEEN NICE

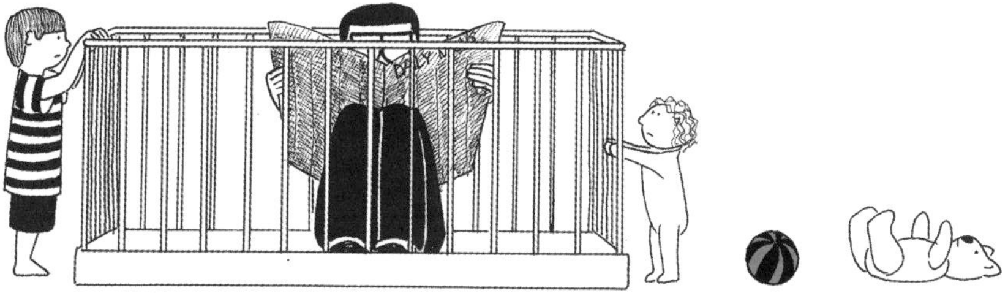

HAVE YOU SEEN THE ADVICE JERRY HALL'S MOTHER GAVE HER WHEN SHE MARRIED MICK JAGGER ?
NOPE
SHE SAID, 'IF YOU WANT TO KEEP YOUR MAN YOU'VE GOT TO BE A CORDON BLEU CHEF IN THE KITCHEN AND A WHORE IN THE BEDROOM'.
MMM
HINT ! HINT!
MARTIN THINKS I SHOULD BUY SOME SEXY UNDERWEAR TO SPICE UP MY MARRIAGE. I CAN'T BELIEVE PEOPLE ACTUALLY **WEAR** THIS STUFF
OH, WELL. IN FOR A PENNY, IN FOR A POUND
LATER
NO, STEPHEN. YOU WERE SUPPOSED TO BUY THE SEXY UNDERWEAR FOR SARAH, NOT FOR YOURSELF !
RIGHTO, MARTIN
YOU WERE RIGHT, DARLING. PEEOW !!
CLUNK!
MUMBLE, MUMBLE, DON'T PUT SAND ON THE GRASS, THOMAS!
SAND BELONGS IN THE SANDPIT. STOP FLICKING IT IN ABIGAIL'S FACE !
AT LEAST HE'S NOT DREAMING ABOUT ANOTHER WOMAN
GET OFF MY BEGONIAS !

THERE'S A STRANGE YELLOW OBJECT IN ABIGAIL'S POOH
IS IT A SWEET ?
NOPE
IS IT ONE OF MY MIGRAINE PILLS ?
NOPE. I THINK I KNOW WHAT IT IS
WHAT ?
FIREMAN SAM'S HELMET
THOMAS WAS LOOKING FOR THAT ALL AFTERNOON

1.
STEPHEN! WONDERFUL NEWS!!
WHAT?
2.
CLOSE YOUR EYES. IT'S A SURPRISE
WE'VE WON THE LOTTERY!
3.
AFTER ALL THIS TIME WE'VE FINALLY WON. I LOVE YOU GOD! I KNEW YOU WERE LISTENING TO ALL THOSE PRAYERS.
COME THIS WAY
4.
SIT DOWN, HERE.
I THINK I'M GOING TO CRY
5.
NO MORE FINANCIAL INSECURITY! NO MORE WORRY! NO MORE PLEADING WITH THE BANK
6.
ABIGAIL'S DONE HER FIRST POOH IN THE POTTY!!

THANK GOD IT'S FRIDAY! TWO WHOLE DAYS WITH SARAH AND THE CHILDREN!
MELODY MAKER
NO MEMOS, NO MEETINGS, NO TEDIOUS OFFICE POLITICS......
NO FAXES! NO DEADLINES TO MEET.......
NO COMPUTER SCREENS! NO CLIENTS TO KEEP HAPPY. JUST ME, MY DARLING WIFE AND OUR TWO LITTLE BUNDLES OF LOVE
THREE DAYS LATER
THANK GOD IT'S MONDAY!
FIVE GLORIOUS DAYS OF FAXES, COMPUTERS, MEMOS, MEETINGS....
TRAINS

WELL, CHILDREN! ISN'T IT NICE HAVING COUSIN TOBY OVER FOR THE AFTERNOON?
YES, DADDY!
1.
I THOUGHT WE COULD TEACH HIM OUR DINOSAUR GAME....... ONE PERSON IS THE DINOSAUR AND THEY GO GROWL, GROWWL, GROWWL!
2.
HE HAS TO CATCH THE OTHER PEOPLE WHO ARE MICE AND THEY GO EEEK! EEEK! EEEK! EEEK!
3.
THEN AT TEA-TIME WE CAN HAVE SCRUMMY SANDWICHES AND CAKE AND GET BIG, FAT TUM-TUMS!!
4.
WHAT WOULD YOU LIKE TO BE, TOBY? DO YOU WANT TO GO GROWWL, GROWWL, GROWWL OR EEEK, EEEK, EEEK?
MUMBLE, MUMBLE
5.
SORRY?
HE SAID, 'GET A LIFE', DADDY
6.

YOU REALLY SHOULD CHANGE YOUR BANK YOU KNOW, DAVID. THIS TELEPHONE BANKING IS BRILLIANT. YOU CAN RING 24 HOURS A DAY AND DO ANY TRANSACTIONS YOU LIKE OVER THE PHONE.....
1.
AH, YES. I'D LIKE TO KNOW THE BALANCE OF MY ACCOUNT, PLEASE.
2.
AT CLOSE OF BUSINESS YESTERDAY YOU HAD A DEBIT OF £2,426.28. YOU HAVE EXCEEDED YOUR OVER-DRAFT LIMIT AND WILL BE CHARGED £20 A DAY PENALTY. WE WILL ALSO BE UNABLE TO HONOUR ANY FURTHER CHEQUES ISSUED BY YOU OR YOUR WIFE. IF YOU ATTEMPT TO USE YOUR CASHCARD AT A SERVICE TILL, THE MACHINE WILL ISSUE NO MONEY AND THE CARD WILL BE RETAINED
THANKS A LOT. BYEEE!
3.
SEE? IT'S SO SIMPLE!
BRILLIANT!
4.
I'LL GO HOME AND RING THEM RIGHT NOW. THANKS FOR THE TIP STEPHEN. CHEERS!
CHEERS!
8
5.
SOB!
6.

1.
HOW ABOUT FRIDAY NIGHT ?
I'M ALWAYS SHATTERED ON FRIDAY NIGHTS
2.
SATURDAY MORNING ?
CAN'T, I'LL BE TAKING THE CHILDREN TO MOTHER'S
3.
GREAT ! LET'S DO IT WHILE THEY ARE AT YOUR MOTHER'S
STEPHEN, I'VE GOT A THOUSAND AND ONE THINGS TO DO THAT DAY ! WHAT ABOUT SUNDAY MORNING?
4.
I'VE PROMISED TO TAKE THE CHILDREN OUT ON THEIR BIKES. HOW ABOUT SUNDAY NIGHT ?
I'M ALWAYS EXHAUSTED AT THE END OF THE WEEKEND. WHAT ABOUT MONDAY NIGHT?
5.
MONDAY NIGHT'S GOOD FOR ME. AROUND NINE O'CLOCK ?
O.K. LET'S INK THAT IN
6.
MONDAY 9.00 P.M. MAKE LOVE
DONK !
SCRIBBLE
SCRIBBLE SCRIBBLE

THAT'S A PINT FOR ALAN A SCOTCH FOR SIMON AND A TOMATO JUICE FOR STEPHEN
A TOMATO JUICE ?
1.
YES, HE'S GOING HOME AT 9.00 TO MAKE LOVE TO HIS WIFE AND HE DOESN'T WANT TO IMPAIR HIS PERFORMANCE
HOW CAN HE BE SURE SHE'LL BE IN THE MOOD ?
2.
THEY'VE PRE-ARRANGED IT. THEY HAVE SUCH BUSY SCHEDULES
YOU'RE JOKING !
3.
PEEP, PEEP PEEP, PEEP
IS THAT ME ?
NO, IT'S STEPHEN
4.
BLAB BLAB BLAB
THAT'S AWFUL. IMAGINE MAKING APPOINTMENTS TO MAKE LOVE TO YOUR OWN WIFE !
5.
DAVID ! CAN YOU MAKE MINE A PINT ?
O.K., STEPHEN !
MUST HAVE HAD A CANCELLATION
6.

HAVE A GOOD DAY, DARLING, AND THANKS AGAIN FOR LOOKING AFTER THE CHILDREN FOR THE WHOLE WEEKEND WHILE I WAS AWAY
TWITCH
1.
TWITCH
SHUFFLE
SHUFFLE
2.
THE BOOKWORM
TWITCH
SHUFFLE
3
PSYCHOLOGY
MEDICINE
TWITCH
4.
TRAINS
TWITCH
SHUFFLE
5.
TWITCH
POST-TRAUMATIC STRESS DISORDER
6.

I'M NOT BAD FOR MY AGE
IF I TILT MY HEAD BACK YOU CAN HARDLY SEE MY THINNING HAIR
2.
AND THE DOUBLE CHIN DISAPPEARS
3.
IF I TENSE MY MUSCLES, MY STOMACH LOOKS QUITE FLAT
4.
AND IF I CLENCH MY BUTTOCKS MY BOTTOM IS QUITE FIRM
5.
FACE FACTS, DARLING. YOU'RE GETTING OLD, BALD AND FAT!
6.

CLAMBER
ARTS
SUNDAY
REVIEW
CLAMBER
1.
DARLING, HAVE WE STILL GOT THAT OLD PLAYPEN SOMEWHERE ?
IT'S IN THE CELLAR
ARTS
SUNDAY
2.
CLAMBER
ARTS
SUNDAY
CLAMBER
REVIEW
3.

1.
THIS FILM DIRECTOR IS ONLY 28 AND HE'S JUST WON AN OSCAR
SPORT
FOOTBALL RESULTS
THE NEWS
2.
AND LOOK AT THIS PRODUCER. HE OWNS A COMPANY WORTH TEN MILLION, AND HE'S EIGHT YEARS YOUNGER THAN ME. IT'S DEPRESSING!
THE NEWS
INTEREST RATE CUT IMMINENT
3.
LOOK AT THIS FOOTBALLER! HE'S RETIRING, AND GUESS HOW OLD HE IS.... 30! IT MAKES ME FEEL SO OLD!
THE NEWS
INTEREST RATE CUT IMMINENT
4.
WHEN I LOOK IN THE MIRROR, DO YOU KNOW WHAT I SEE? MY FATHER! I LOOK MORE LIKE HIM EVERY DAY. MY HAIR IS THINNING. MY WAIST IS EXPANDING. I CAN'T BEAR IT. I WANT TO BE YOUNG AGAIN!
THE NEWS
INTEREST RATE CUT IMMINENT
5.
STEPHEN, DON'T BE SO NEGATIVE. MOST PEOPLE SAY MIDDLE-AGE IS THE BEST TIME OF THEIR LIFE
DON'T SAY THOSE WORDS!
6.
WHICH WORDS?
MIDDLE-AGE

1.
SOB! SOB!
2.
THOMAS, WHAT'S THE MATTER?
3.
WHAT IS IT, SON?
4.
WHY ARE YOU CRYING?
5.
SHALL I TELL HIM, THOMAS?
YES
6.
HE DOESN'T WANT YOU TAKING HIM TO PLAYGROUP IN THOSE SHORTS

MORE SEX AND MORE MONEY MORE SEX AND MORE MONEY...
2.
WHAT ARE YOU PRAYING FOR, DARLING ?
WORLD PEACE AND AN END TO GLOBAL WARMING
3.
HE'S A VERY SPECIAL MAN
MORE SEX AND MORE MONEY MORE SEX AND MORE MONEY...

THAT WAS THE MOST PASSIONATE LOVE-MAKING WE'VE HAD FOR A LONG TIME. YOUR H.R.T. PATCH IS WORKING WONDERS
1.
YES, I'M REALLY FEELING LIKE A WHOLE WOMAN AGAIN
AMAZING WHAT A LITTLE BIT OF HORMONE CAN DO. HOW LONG DO YOU HAVE TO KEEP IT ON FOR?
2.
UNTIL THE COURSE HAS FINISHED. WHERE IS IT ?
WHERE'S WHAT ?
3.
MY PATCH ! I WAS WEARING IT WHEN WE GOT INTO BED. IT'S GONE !
4.
IT'S DISAPPEARED ! IT WAS ON MY THIGH AND IT'S DISAPPEARED !
5.
I'VE LOST MY PRECIOUS PATCH !
DON'T FUSS, DARLING ! IT CAN'T HAVE GONE FAR !
6.